ROBERT JOHNSON

by Samuel Charters

with photos
of Robert Johnson's
Mississippi delta country
by the author

© 1973
Oak Publications/New York
Music Sales Limited/London

for Country Joe McDonald

Joe—After not seeing each other
for so many years
the first thing we talked about—
Robert Johnson, again—so this is for you.

Book design by Jean Hammons and Mei Mei Sanford

Robert Johnson died without copyrighting any of his
songs, and there was no copyright claim made by any of
his family; so the songs are what is called "public domain,"
meaning that they cannot be claimed or copyrighted by
anyone.

© 1973 Oak Publications
33 West 60th Street
New York, New York 10023

Music Sales Limited
78 Newman Street
London, W1E 4JZ

Music Sales Australia (Pty) Ltd.
27 Clarendon Street
Artarmon, Sydney NSW

Quick Fox Ltd.
40 Nugget Avenue
Agincourt, Ontario

Library of Congress Catalog Card Number 72-97852
International Standard Book Number 0-8256-0059-6

CONTENTS

ROBERT JOHNSON

I first started looking for Robert Johnson some time in the mid-1950's. I don't remember when it was, what year, what month—I probably wrote it down somewhere but I wouldn't know where to look for it. I just remember coming into San Antonio grimy and red-eyed from days of hitch hiking to get there, clothes sweaty and wrinkled—going into the Greyhound bus depot to wash up—then walking up and down the streets of the black neighborhoods asking people if they'd heard of a singer who'd made some blues records in town. The only thing I knew about him was the records, and that had been twenty years before, and it wasn't enough. I didn't have the name of a girl, the address of a boarding house or a cheap hotel. Nobody I asked had ever heard of him. Years went by before I finally found somebody who had—and then I began to find that other people had heard of him, and it was possible to begin to think of the man as something more than a name on a record. The same thing has happened to Robert Johnson's music, to the handful of blues he recorded in San Antonio and Dallas those years ago. It was music that only a few had heard, and years passed, and then it was music that almost everybody had heard, even if they didn't know where it had come from.

I don't think it's important to say that any singer is "greatest"—what do you mean by the word and how do you compare one against another—but Robert Johnson's voice has touched us all. It's hard to think of any other singer who did so much in so little time, with so little creative space to work in. When the sessions were done no one thought that the music of a young Mississippi field hand would ever go beyond the small world it had come from—it was the same for all of the Mississippi delta men who managed to make records during those years—but it is music that has reached, has stretched out, until it's become part of the world's culture, part of the sound the world grows up in now. It is still only a sound to part of the world—to the people who need the sense of what he had to sing about, who feel the urgencies and lonelinesses that he felt. If I went back to the streets of San Antonio and asked again at some of the barber shops, some of the street corners—if I asked some of the old men sitting on the benches again—they wouldn't remember anymore about a young, drifting Mississippi blues singer than they did the first time I asked—but I think some of their children would now, and that's what Robert Johnson's music is about.

Until his sister was found recently in Washington, D. C. Robert Johnson's life was one of the elusive mysteries of the blues. Other blues singers had met him—they remembered seeing him at a club or a dance, traveling with him for a few days or a few months—some had drifted through the place in the delta where he'd grown up—but they still were only momentary glimpses of his life. It was difficult to get a clear image of either Robert or the life he'd lived in his short years. His sister hadn't known that his music had become the root source for a whole generation of blues and rock and roll musicians. She'd kept the photos she had, but she didn't talk about him, and she didn't think anyone even remembered him. In the almost twenty years of trying to find out something about his life, the only things that had been found were other singers' reminiscences and a death certificate. It said that Robert Johnson—"musician"—died in Greenwood, Mississippi on August 16, 1938. His age was given as 26. It was the place other musicians remembered he died, and it's about the time he was supposed to have been murdered. But I always could remember a conversation in Friars Point, in the delta, a buzzing soft day and a man and woman, old and lined, standing watching a friend pull down the wooden walls of an old shack in Friars Point's ramshackle black section.

"Robert Johnson," the man said, looking away from me with old, cautious eyes, "We had a lot of boys around here named Johnson, and there was that other boy, Robert, who made the records." He was remembering Robert Nighthawk, who'd lived in Friars Point. "You say he was stabbed?"

"That's what I heard," I said.

"What was the name of the boy who was stabbed?" asking his wife, standing nervously with a black sweater hanging loose from her shoulders.

"It was 1937 or 1938," I went on.

"That boy's name was Robert." His wife, thinking, in a low voice. "He might have been one of the Johnsons, but I don't know if he was stabbed."

"It seems to me that that boy was stabbed *and* shot, so that's different, and there was another . . . just to the north of town . . . but he was shot."

I had an almost choking sense of the Mississippi past that clung to them, with its raw smell of violence.

"We had another boy that was killed on the street . . . in town, around then." The man's thin voice had gotten softer.

"But that was a beating. They beat him," his wife said, almost in a whisper, looking at her husband.

It was a warm day, birds in the vine straggled trees around us, dogs barking. "Could one of them be the boy you mean?" The man stood uncomfortably, his friend stopping to look at us, holding his old hammer against the bib of his overalls. "No," I said, "I don't think so," going with slow steps back to the car. It could have been Robert Johnson there, one of those hot August nights in a shack along the levee. It could have been Robert Johnson in Greenwood, that August 16th in 1938.

Even with the death certificate it was still difficult to get any clear information about Robert or his life. It said that he was born in Hazelhurst, that his father was named Nonah Johnson, and his mother Julia Major. The informant was someone named Jim Moore, and without talking to him there was no way to be sure how well he knew Robert. The death certificate wasn't signed, so there was no way of finding out if the sheriff in Greenwood had been at the death scene. The Hazelhurst birthplace also made the death certificate questionable; since Hazelhurst is south of Jackson, about thirty-five miles out from it on Route 51, in Copiah County, and everybody else who knew Robert had always said he was from the delta, north of Jackson in Tunica County. But sharecropper families moved around a lot—from one stretch of shacks to another stretch of shacks, going on with their few possessions piled in the back of somebody's truck or—in the years before the first World War when Robert was born—in somebody's wagon. What other people who knew him remembered was that he and his

5

family—his mother, whose name was remembered as Mary, her children and his step-father, Robert "Dusty" Johnson—moved into a cabin in a shack community close to the Mississippi River levee in the delta when he was five, and he grew up there. Son House remembers that when he met him, "He was living on a plantation out from Robinsonville. On a man's place called Mr. Richard Lellman." Son's memory was good, the name is painted on one of the buildings of the farm, R. Leatherman, and the plantation is still there. It's the stretch of flat, dusty fields along the river, and the row of crumbling shacks called Commerce.

To get to Commerce the best road is down from Memphis, down through the rows of one story houses in the Memphis suburbs on Route 61. The houses go down to the Mississippi line, thinning out as you drive, the white porches standing back of their patches of lawn. Just over the state border you get the first Mississippi gun shops—"Guns—Ammunition." Firearms are everywhere in Mississippi, mostly for hunting, but there in the house if they're needed for anything else. You go through a range of low dirt hills, then you drop onto the flat plain of the delta, like a hot drab brown table spread out around you. The highway runs through the fields, the cotton rows stretching on both sides, off to the river to the west, off to the first low, dark stretch of high ground to the east. You can follow the dirt roads going off from the highway by the clouds of dust rising behind the pickup trucks going off to the sheds. Robinsonville's about 27 miles south of the center of Memphis—16 miles south of the Tennessee line—Commerce is at the end of a dirt road 4½ miles west of Robinsonville. There's no sign for Commerce—it's just one of the shack communities strung along a road in northern Mississippi. There's no store, nothing except a church. You have to walk into Robinsonville to get things you need. If you drive down the road on a work day there's nobody in the shacks but the women and children. The men are in the fields. You climb up on a weathered board porch and knock on a sagging screen door. Children rubbed with dust over their ragged overalls stand uncertainly a few feet behind you. The women shake their heads in quick nervous movements. "No, I don't know nobody been here long. This is Commerce, alright, but nobody been here long that I know of."

The crude shacks don't have any sense of permanence as you drive slowly back to Robinsonville. The levee, just beyond the end of Commerce, and the brick buildings of the land owners seem to be the only things with any permanence. The shacks are crude pine board boxes, propped up on concrete blocks—at some point in their poor past covered with brown building paper scored to look like brick. The corners of the paper flap in the wind where they've torn loose. Commerce looks no different from the other clusters of shacks scattered down the delta. As you climb the levee behind Commerce you can see the buildings dotting the earth, small, dirt-colored clumps strung out on the farm roads. When people remember Robert's father as the small man they called "Robert Dusty," his clothes covered with dust when he walked the roads, they're remembering him on the dry rutted stretch of road from Commerce to Robinsonville.

Although most of the families living in the area around Robinsonville are new, there are still some older people who can dimly remember Robert Johnson, even though it's been more than forty years since he was living down the road with his family. An old man named Preacher Brown, who lives a few miles south of

Commerce, remembers that Robert was just playing the harmonica before he left. But when he came back he had a guitar and "a lot of girls." Robert wouldn't have been much different from the cluster of adolescents who were leaning against a shed behind one of the houses on a Sunday afternoon. They had on white shirts and good pants, and they were laughing with each other, joking noisily. Not any of the kind of complicated word play of the rural South, just telling stories about girls from other places along the river, about jobs and bosses. Thin, gawky, stringy muscles under their starched shirts; their dark faces shining as they laughed. They were about the age Robert was when he left, and in two or three years most of them will be gone, like him, looking for something that they can't find in the poor rows of shacks, in the heavy dirt stretch of dull brown fields behind them.

The clearest glimpse we have of the adolescent Robert Johnson is Son House's memory of the skinny kid who came into the dances where Son was playing with Patton and Willie Brown. It isn't much, but it at least picks up his life at the moment his life as a musician was starting—or just at the moment it did start. Of all the people who influenced his music Son was the most influential, so the essential outline of what he remembers must be true.

"...we'd all play for the Saturday night balls and there'd be this little boy standing around. That was Robert Johnson. He was just a little boy then. He blew a harmonica and he was pretty good with that, but he wanted to play a guitar. When we'd leave at night to go play for the balls, he'd slip off and come over to where we were. His mother and step-father didn't like for him to go out to those Saturday night balls because the guys were so rough. But he'd slip away, anyway. Sometimes he'd even wait until his mother went to bed and then he'd get out the window and make it to where we were. He'd get where Willie and I were and sit right down on the floor and watch from one to the other. And when we'd get a break and want to rest some, we'd set the guitars up in the corner and go out in the cool. Robert would watch and see which way we'd gone and he would pick one of them up. And such another racket you never heard! It'd make the people mad, you know. They'd come out and say, 'Why don't y'all go in there and get that guitar away from that boy! He's running people crazy with it.' I'd come back in and I'd scold him about it. 'Don't do that, Robert. You drive people nuts. You can't play nothing. Why don't you blow the harmonica for 'em?' But he didn't want to blow that. Still, he didn't care how I'd get after him about it. He'd do it anyway.

"Well, he didn't care anything about working in the fields and his father was so tight on him about slipping out and coming where we were, so he just got the idea he'd run away from home. He was living on a plantation out from Robinsonville. On a man's place called Mr. Richard Lellman. And he ran away. Didn't want to work on any farms.

"He stayed, looked like to me, about six months. Willie and I were playing again out at a little place east of Robinsonville called Banks, Mississippi. We were playing there one Saturday night and, all of a sudden, somebody came in through the door. Who but him! He had a guitar swinging on his back. I said, 'Bill!' He said, 'Huh?' I said 'Look who's coming in the door.' He looked and said, 'Yeah, Little Robert.' I said, 'And he's got a guitar.' And Willie and I laughed about it. Robert finally wiggled through the crowd and got to where we

7

were. He spoke, and I said, 'Well, boy, you still got a guitar, huh? What do you do with that thing? You can't do nothing with it.' He said, 'Well, I'll tell you what.' I said, 'What?' He said, 'Let me have your seat a minute.' So I said, 'All right, and you better do something with it, too,' and I winked my eye at Willie. So he sat down there and finally got started. And man! He was so good! When he finished all our mouths were standing open. I said, 'Well, ain't that fast! He's gone now!'

"So he hung around about a week or more, and I gave him a little instruction. Said, 'Now, Robert. You going around playing for these Saturday night balls. You have to be careful 'cause you mighty crazy about the girls. When you playing for these balls and these girls get full of that corn whiskey and snuff mixed together, and you be playing a good piece and they like it and come up and call you 'Daddy, play it again, Daddy'—well, don't let it run you crazy. You liable to get killed.' He must not have paid it much attention. He laughed it off, you know. I said, 'You gotta be careful about that 'cause a lot of times, they do that, and they got a husband or a boy friend standing right over in the corner. You getting all excited over 'em and you don't know what you're doing. You get hurt.' I gave him the best instruction. So he said, 'Okay.' Finally, he left and went somewhere else again with his guitar. We heard a couple of his pieces come out on records. Believe the first one I heard was *Terraplane Blues.* Jesus, it was good. We all admired it. Said, 'That boy is really going places.' So he left and went out there from Greenwood, Mississippi. Somewhere out in there. . ."

Greenwood is on U.S. 82, in the west central part of the Yazoo Delta, in the rolling farm country that starts a little way back from the Mississippi River. Robert started the way most young blues singers started, by forcing one of the older men to stand aside, to give him room. Lightning Hopkins remembers doing it to Blind Lemon Jefferson, most of the Mississippi singers remember some moment when they stood up and did it themselves. Johnny Shines did it with Howling Wolf, and what he felt must have been what Robert felt when he made Son House give up his chair in that dance hall in Banks, Mississippi.*

"Well, I like Howling Wolf's style, but I couldn't understand it. And I just hung around till I begin to dig the guy and I really came in knowledge of what he was doing. See, I went after him. He was playing one Saturday night for Will (Will Weilers, who had a dance hall in Arkansas), and he set his guitar down for a rest, as all musicians do, you know. Well, this particular night everything changed, they started calling me Little Wolf, because when he came back I had the joint rocking. With Wolf's style, you know, the Wolf's numbers. I mean, it was just that easy this particular night. I could see what he was doing and understand it. All before hand it was all, I say, Greek to me, but just in a few minutes time I really begin to understand what he was doing so when he went on his break I tried it. When he came back I had the joint rocking.

"I was afraid of Wolf. Just like you would be of some kind of beast or something. Because it was an old saying, you know, people thought about magic and all such things as that and I come along and say a guy that played like Wolf, he'd sold his soul to the devil. And at that time Wolf had the most beautiful skin anybody ever seen in your life, look like you can just blow on it and it'd riffle.

*Many of Johnny Shine's quotes are from Peter Gurelnick's excellent interview with him that was published in *Rolling Stone Magazine.*

And I was kind of afraid of Wolf, I mean just to walk up and put your hand on him, no I didn't touch him. . ."

What Son remembers with Robert is so close to what Johnny remembers with Howling Wolf that it must have been true—as Son remembers it, as it sounds in the blues Robert recorded a few scant years later.

Scant—it seems to be the word to use for Robert. There were so few scant years, so scant few stories that people remember about him. Of the two blues men who met him later, which one met him first? Did he first travel with Johnny Shines? Or did he come to knock on Henry Townsend's door first? Maybe if the two of them talked it over they could decide. Or it could have been that Robert first traveled with Johnny, then went off on his own and met Townsend, then ran into Johnny later again. Years blur, the edge goes off days and times. How do you remember back ten years, twenty years, thirty years? At different times both Johnny and Henry tried. Sitting late one night in Johnny Shine's apartment in Chicago, drinking with Johnny and Walter Horton, snow on the streets and the windows across the street still strung with Christmas ornaments and the red lights shining a flickering red glow over the ice below and into the apartments across the way. It was 1965, just a few days before Johnny went into the studio and recorded his own version of Robert's *Terraplane Blues.* He and Walter decided it must have been in 1933. "I was seventeen or eighteen when I went off to Arkansas and it was right at that time that I met him."

Johnny remembers him from West Helena, Arkansas.

". . . A friend of mine carried me down to Helena, Arkansas, where Robert was, he wanted me to meet Robert. Because this friend of mine thought I were good. Robert just picked songs out of the air. You could have the radio on, and he'd be talking to you and you'd have no idea he'd be thinking of it because he'd go right on talking. But later he'd play that song note for note. All kinds of songs. Hillbilly, blues, and all the rest. . .

"Robert was a very friendly person, even though he was sulky at times, you know. And I hung around Robert for quite a while. One evening he disappeared. He was a kind of peculiar fellow. Robert'd be standing up playing some place, playing like nobody's business. At that time it was a hustle with him as well as a pleasure. And money'd be coming from all directions. But Robert'd just pick up and walk off and leave you standing there playing. And you wouldn't see Robert no more maybe in two or three weeks . . . So Robert and I, we began journeying off. I was just, matter of fact, tagging along."

The life that Robert was leaving behind was the hard, poor life of farming in the Mississippi delta. The sticking red mud of the spring when it's time to do the plowing, the sweltering summer days weeding cotton under the blaze of the sun, bent over the handle of the hoe, then the last of the summer, bending down to pick the cotton, dragging the cotton sack behind in the row. A hard life even if you have something to show for it, an intolerable life if the social system keeps you down there, in the cotton rows, with nothing but a worn body and anger at the end of your years. But the people who broke out of it—men and women—will say that they had moments of happiness, despite the labor, despite the poverty. Muddy Waters described his life in Rolling Fork, a small town south west of Greenwood, west of Yazoo City, almost to the Mississippi River.

". . . My daddy was a farmer; he raised hawgs and chickens. Grew watermelons. We had a l'il—oh, two-room shack and there was a creek—Deer Creek—come right up in the steps of the back porch. I was always playin' in the creek and gettin' dirty and my sisters called me Muddy Waters then. Mama died when I was about three and my grandmammy carried me up to Clarksdale, and that's where I was raised. I went to school but they didn't give you too much schoolin' because just as soon as you was big enough you get to workin' in the fields. I guess I was a big boy for my age, but I was just a boy and they put me to workin' right along side the men. I handled the plough, chopped cotton, did all of them things. . ." And he went on at another time to say that—with all of it—it hadn't been intolerable.

"I worked on the farm, I worked in the city, and I worked all around. This is at the time I was living with my grandmother. I wouldn't say I was supporting myself, but I worked. I didn't get very much schooling. The school system wasn't too good, and, number one, I really didn't have the time, I thought, in those days to be bothered with it. I didn't really know that you need schooling down through the years. It's one mistake I made—but the rest of it down there was great."

But Robert left, as Muddy was to leave afterwards, as other singers had left before him. It doesn't do much good to try to trace it on a map. He wandered, drifted around, moved from town to town, from woman to woman. Johnny Shines remembers him from West Helena, Arkansas, the first town you'd get to if you went west to get out of the delta. The only bridge over the Mississippi between Memphis and Greenville, 165 miles south, crosses the levees of Powell, Mississippi, and gets you on one of the roads between Helena and West Helena. Helena itself is a rundown river town, with a few blocks of stores and a straggling white neighborhood up on the higher ground. There is a black district—some dirty brick buildings along Walnut Street—along the railroad tracks on Mobile. At night the windows—with their faded homemade curtains—are shining flowered openings in the blackness. The singers mostly went on to the square shack area in West Helena, five miles further west on the bluffs. It's close to the stacks and cylinders of the Chicago Mill and Lumber Company. Inside the fence there are piles and piles of logs, boys picking up slabs to burn in the shack stoves. The houses are mostly made out of the same wood—green-painted, white-painted, unpainted—tin-roofed, most of them stained with rust. The grocery stores are Chinese, S. L. Wong & Co., Wing Guay, Hom Kim, the buildings the same dilapidated wood frames, with larger porches and worn metal advertising signs. It still has a little music in it—a man standing on a porch says there's a little band that goes out and plays a little. "They mostly get jobs in the Veteran's Hut out on the highway."

Big Joe Williams, who scratched his way across most of the delta country in the '20's and '30's remembers that there was usually something going on in West Helena.

"There was a big sawmill there—I don't remember the name of it—but they always had a gang of people working for them, and there'd always be a lot of money because of the jobs. I used to go there to play and I could always pick up something, people there, you know, had most of them just come out of Mississippi anyway, so they wanted to hear the blues."

A few brick buildings have gone up in the area—one or two of the streets close to the highway have been paved—but the rest of it looks just like it must have looked in the early 1930's.

For some of the time in the mid-1930's he was living in Helena with a woman named Esther Lockwood, and he stayed with her when he came into town. She was considerably older than Robert, and had a son only a few years younger. The son learned to play the guitar listening to his stepfather play, and he still is known as Robert Junior Lockwood. Robert seems to have moved in with his mother about 1933 or 1934, and Robert Jr. remembers that it was Johnson's influence that started him on the guitar.

"Robert Johnson was my beginning. He came along and taught me how to play. In the beginning I wanted to play a piano. Really my ambition was to play a piano until Robert came along. He was doing such a good job with the guitar I just switched. Now I don't even think about it. . ."*

Some of the time that Shines knew Robert he was staying with Esther Lockwood, and he went over to the house to talk to him. It was from Helena and West Helena that they started their drifting. Robert Junior remembered that Robert just came in and out of town, giving him lessons when he was home. When Robert was killed Esther took her son with her to St. Louis, in 1939.

Robert and Johnny traveled any way they could, with anybody else who was with them. They didn't get away from the racism in the North either.

". . .We stopped at this place in Illinois and the guy asked us to play a piece. So Robert starts out playing and me right with him, and they tried to get us to stay there, so we stayed a couple of nights, and the people at that time paid 25 cents a head to come in and see what the colored guys looked like. And that wasn't in the South either. Well that just shows how unthoughtful sometimes people can be."

I think of Robert traveling in cars a lot, with anybody he could get a lift from. I think of him standing on a sidewalk outside a barroom, trying to get a ride. "You going to Memphis? Or just to West Memphis. I just have this guitar and I can get a bus out of there." The guitar with him everywhere he went, hanging down his back the way Son House remembers. When I think of Robert traveling I think of a picture from Louisiana of one of the bands, Evan Thomas's band, standing around an open convertible under the trees in the country outside of New Orleans. They're in shirt sleeves, the trombone player, Joe Avery, in his undershirt and suspenders, the light from the sun filtering down through the trees, and they looked loose and easy, by themselves on a back road in the slow afternoon. Robert probably did a lot of traveling in cars like that, with other singers, with men he knew, going from one back country road house to another, or just getting to someplace where he could take a bus. Sometimes he just stood along the road and tried to catch a lift. As he sang in one of his greatest blues,

> I went to the crossroads, fell down on my knees.
> I went to the crossroads, fell down on my knees.
> I asked the Lord above, have mercy, save poor Bob if you please.
>
> Uumh, standing at the crossroads I tried to flag a ride.
> Standing at the crossroads I tried to flag a ride.
> Ain't nobody seem to know me, everybody pass me by.

Henry Townsend tried to remember when it was he'd first met Robert Johnson, sitting in the front room of the new apartment he'd just moved into in one

*From "Living Blues" Magazine's interview with Robert Junior Lockwood by William Cummerow.

11

of St. Louis's first integrated housing developments in 1962. I'd brought down copies of the new lp we'd recorded together the summer before and he was playing it for friends over the phone—while the rest of us were trying vanilla ice cream and bourbon on a hot summer St. Louis night. He was sure it was 1935—two years after Robert had started drifting with Johnny Shines.

"... I was living on, I believe it was 2320 Carr Street during that time, and I was playing at Ernest Walker's 'House Party' on Jefferson. Robert Johnson had come over to find me, and he was a stranger in the town so he told me, 'Look, I've heard about you.' He was just traveling through and he says, 'Where you working at tonight?' so I told him and he says, 'Can I come over?' and I said 'Yeah,' so he come over to Walker's...

Well, we sat in the backyard and that fellow, he went over some guitar and I thought, well, this guy's got it. I mean he was amazing. I was a little bit older than him, but I didn't think anybody had any seniority over me on the guitar, but this guy made me look little. During the time I was fixing to leave town, really, and he played for Ernest Walker for about three weeks and I came back and he stayed with me another week over there, for a very small scale, of course. He held the job until I came back and the truth is it was Robert's job when I came back. Robert continued until he was ready to leave; then the boss put me back to work. Robert was very decent about it, I mean we worked together, but as far as the job was concerned it belonged to Robert . . . I don't really know where he was going when he left. He said he was going to Chicago. . ."

Shines must have come up with him, or it was a different time, but Shines also remembers a moment of Robert's playing in St. Louis.

"He was a guy that could make a song sound good with a slide, regardless of its content or nature. His guitar seemed to talk—repeat and say words with him like no one else in the world could. One time in St. Louis we were playing one of the songs that Robert would like to play with someone once in a great while. *Come On In My Kitchen.* He was playing very slow and passionate, and when we had quit, I noticed no one was saying anything. Then I realized they were crying—both women and men."

Ramshackle, smoky dark St. Louis, with its streets and streets of slums—mostly torn down now and empty lots waiting for something else to be built up on them. High fronted stone and brick buildings, with high, crumbling elegant windows set into weathered, paint peeled strips of frame. In winter, rags stuffed around cracks in the windows to keep out the wind, in summer, windows pushed up and flowered curtains blowing out over the street. Market Street, Delmar Avenue, Lucas Avenue—the Lucas Avenue Edith Johnson sang about,

> Give me a nickle's worth of liver,
> Give me a dime's worth of stew,
> And I can feed everybody on Lucas Avenue.

Still a blues town in the thirties, though the most successful singer living in St. Louis, Lonnie Johnson, had moved out of the city. The Melrose brothers were coming down from Chicago to look for talent, Jessie Stone still had his record shop and talent agency. Charley Jordan and Peetie Wheatstraw were in town, there were clubs and cafes on every corner—the clubs mostly just old store fronts that had been taken over and decorated—new fronts put on—or corner wooden buildings that had been old saloons. The Rosebud Cafe was still open—the old

Rosebud that had been the center of some of St. Louis's first ragtime in the 1890's—with the Turpin brothers, Tom and Charley, still running it. Tom had been one of the first—one of the very first—ragtime composers, in 1897, and everybody played in the Rosebud, from Scott Joplin to Louis Chauvin. Charley had a theatre that booked in most of the touring black stage acts. Robert probably lived somewhere around Turpin's neighborhood, in the black slum that had grown up just west of the St. Louis business district, Robert's blues and Turpin's ragtime in the same few blocks along the street car tracks. Usually when I saw Big Joe Williams and his cousin J. D. Short in St. Louis they stayed in rooms around that part of the city—run-down furnished rooms in shabby buildings. Hallways marked and scarred, door locks broken in, and old linoleum peeling up off the floors.

And like Big Joe and J. D., Robert Johnson living there in one of the rooms—nervous, small and thin, "round shouldered" as Henry Townsend remembers him, probably living in one of the rooms upstairs over a store. I always think of him someplace along Delmar or Lucas, sleeping late, the woman he was staying with already gone out when he got up from his late musician's sleep. Standing at the window for a little, watching the people going by selling things on the streets, men hanging out on the corners, sitting on the steps, women leaning out windows, working at house cleaning. No jobs in St. Louis in 1935. Then out to one of the little cafes for something to eat, and in the afternoon drifting into a card game in one of the back rooms, or playing the guitar in the back of a music store or over in somebody else's room. The other guitar players in town knew where he was. When he left he told Henry Townsend he was going to Chicago, and he must have gotten there, since Shines remembers that it was in Chicago that he finally lost track of him, but he couldn't have been in Chicago long. When he sang about it, in *Sweet Home Chicago*, he sang,

I'm cryin', hey, baby, don't you want to go,
To the land of California, to my sweet home Chicago.

Whatever kind of time he had there he wandered back again. Train? Back on the Illinois Central? Bus? A car with somebody? The blues singers stayed together, drove their cars together, hung out together, hustling together for whatever they could get, from money, to drinks, to women—the life of the blues, the life that went into their music.

Out of all this wandering there's finally a date. We have five dates in Robert's life—the dates of his recording sessions in Texas in 1936 and 1937. Five days when we know where Robert Johnson was and what he was doing, at least for the hours that he was recording. Monday, November 23, 1936, Thursday, November 26, and Friday, November 27, he was in San Antonio, Texas. Seven months later, June 19, a Saturday, and the next day, Sunday, June 20, 1937, he was in Dallas. The recordings were done by Don Law, who was working in Texas for the American Recording Corporation. Robert was brought to him by one of A.R.C.'s record scouts, Ernie Oertle, who heard Robert play in Mississippi. Law, in 1936, had not done a great deal of recording, but he later went to work for Columbia Records, as a country and western producer, and even after his recent retirement is still producing some of the artists he started working with in the forties. Oertle, who could have told us more about Robert, died of a heart attack two years after the second sessions. Law insists that Robert was 19, and that he was just off the plantation. He could be right, but Son House remembers him leaving the country when he was still in his early teens, and Johnny Shines and Henry Townsend were with him earlier than 1936. Law's description of him is similar to theirs. "He was a little above medium height, not real jet black, but real black. He had the most beautiful hands I've ever seen—long slender fingers. By and large he was a very good looking boy."

Another singer from the delta, Honey Boy Edwards has recently described Robert as being tall, brown skinned, with one bad eye, and playing on a Sears Roebuck Stella guitar—but he must be confusing his memory of him with somebody else, since the men who traveled and played with him—as well as Don Law—all remember the same slight, dark nervous drifter. If it is his death certificate that's been found, and if the person giving information to the police knew Robert well, then Law is wrong and he was in his twenties when he met Shines and Henry Townsend, but he seemed younger to them. As Townsend said,

"At the time I met him he was fresh out of Memphis, he'd been playing out there . . . he was a dark skinned fellow, kind of round shouldered, very small and very young. I thought he must have been teenage. Of course I didn't know whether he was eighteen or seventeen or fifteen, but he was a teenager at that time. But he didn't like the title of being kid. . ."

Johnny Shines was seventeen when he met Robert in 1933, and he thought Robert was maybe a year older than he was. If he was older he didn't give anyone the sense of being older, and the blues he did had an almost painful immaturity. When they were with him they thought of him as young, but as Townsend added, "He was a man as far as he was concerned. . ."

Out of these few days, these few hours, we have some of our clearest glimpses of him. Frank Driggs, of Columbia Records, talked to Law many years later and wrote,

". . . Don Law considered himself responsible for Johnson, found him a room in a boarding house and told him to get some sleep so he would be ready to begin recording at ten the following morning. Law then joined his wife and some friends for dinner at the Gunter Hotel. He had scarcely begun dinner when he was summoned to the phone. A policeman was calling from the city jail. Johnson had been picked up on a vagrancy charge. Law rushed down to the jail, found Johnson beaten up, his guitar smashed; the cops had not only picked him up but had worked him over. With some difficulty, Law managed to get Johnson freed in his custody, whisked him back to the boarding house, gave him forty-five cents for breakfast, and told him to stay in the house and not to go out for the rest of the evening. Law returned to the hotel, only to be called to the phone again. This time it was Johnson. Fearing the worst, Law asked, 'What's the matter now?' Johnson replied, 'I'm lonesome.' Puzzled, Law said, 'You're lonesome? What do you mean, you're lonesome?' Johnson replied, 'I'm lonesome and there's a lady here. She wants fifty cents and I lacks a nickel. . .'"

In another interview Law added that ". . . apparently he had nothing to do and he went into some dive where he played for nickels, and the place was raided."

San Antonio is a long way from the delta—a long way from Memphis. It's 602 miles from Jackson, Mississippi, to San Antonio by car—and it's more than that in the feel of the country, the style of the people. The Alamo, the old fort, is still standing close to the center of the city—in a dry square with office buildings around it. The San Antonio River drifts and turns through the town, the banks turned into a kind of park, with trees and paths under the old metal bridges. The black section is back behind the Alamo, mostly wooden houses, set back off the street, or brick apartments over the store fronts. The sessions were done in an improvised studio set up in a room in the Gunter Hotel and Robert could have walked across the Alamo Square getting to the hotel. In some sections of San Antonio it's more of a Mexican town than it is anything else, and sometimes it seems that the blacks and whites have, on some level of communication, a kind of unspoken sense of standing together against the Mexicans, who don't speak a lot of English, or have much feeling for the importance of Texas. In the thirties, San Antonio had a lot of music, most of it big jazz orchestras. Don Albert's band was one of them—Boots Douglas was leading Boots and His Buddies. Less than twenty years later, trying to find somebody who'd seen Robert Johnson, I talked with people from Don Albert's band, and went along with Boots and his old band on a reunion, but none of them could remember a Mississippi guitar player in town to do some blues sessions.

Law, as the Texas branch manager for A.R.C., was working with all kinds of musicians, and he was doing some sessions with Mexican musicians at the same time that he was working with Robert.

"He was very reticent and very shy. This was the first time he'd been to what he considered a big city, the first time he'd been off the plantation. I had some Mexican musicians in the studio, and I said 'Robert, sing something for us.' He wouldn't face us. He finally turned his back, turned into a corner and sang a song."

It could have been something else bothering Robert. I was standing in a club with Lightning Hopkins in Houston and he listened to some Mexican music over the juke box, swallowed some beer and shook his head. "Always watch out for them Mexicans with the six string guitar. They can do so much on it they'll kill you with it."

There were eight blues the first day. Robert began recording on Monday, November 23, 1936—the first song was *Kind Hearted Woman. Come on In My Kitchen* was done at the session, along with *Ramblin' On My Mind* and *I Believe I'll Dust My Broom*. The next session, three days later, was less successful—only a single blues, *32-20 Blues*, and that was something he'd learned from a Skip James record. The next day, Friday, November 27, began with the jump song *They're Red Hot* and the blues *Dead Shrimp Blues*—then, in one outburst, in a kind of musical possession, he did *Cross Road Blues, Walkin' Blues, Last Fair Deal Gone Down, Preachin' Blues,* and *If I Had Possession Over Judgement Day,* some of the greatest blues he was to record.

The days turned, the winter sloughed past with its rain and mud and streaked roads of sticking ruts between the little farm towns—the Mississippi levee towns —where Robert did most of his playing. The song that Son House remembers hearing, *Terraplane Blues,* was the first thing that came out. After it was *Last Fair Deal Gone Down.* The two records were probably all that Robert ever heard. Seven months after the San Antonio sessions he was in Dallas to record for Don Law again. The first day, Saturday, June 19, 1937, there were three songs, the first of them *Stones In My Passway.* The next day he did ten songs, beginning with *Hell Hound On My Trail,* and the next to last *Love In Vain.* Dallas is a different city than San Antonio, crowded and uneasy, with some of the strain of cities like Cleveland or Providence—northern in its heavy business emphasis, as southern as the other Texas cities in its racial attitudes. There's no way to know if he stayed there, if he was in just long enough to get to the studio. It isn't as far to get to as San Antonio—if he had somebody to drive with he could be back in Mississippi, or even Memphis in a long day's driving.

The drifting started again. As Walter Horton, the harmonica player who worked with Shines, said, thinking about Robert that night in Shines' apartment, "... If anybody said to him 'Let's go,' it didn't matter to him where it was they were going, he'd just take off and go. It didn't matter what time of day or night it was ..." Where did he go, those last months? Who was he with? Maybe someday a woman from one of the levee towns will begin talking about a singer she knew once, when she was young. Someone who ran a dance hall out along one of the dusty roads going across the delta fields will remember a thin young singer who just had a record out, and who played some guitar and did some blues in his place.

Law would eventually have gotten Robert back into the studio to record again, but he heard from John Hammond, who was organizing another Carnegie Hall concert to follow his brilliantly successful "Spirituals To Swing" concert in New York the year before. Hammond wanted to use Robert Johnson. Law said, "I think you're making a mistake, because if you put him up on the stage at Carnegie Hall, he'll die of fright." But, despite his misgivings, Law sent Ernie Oertle to get in touch with Robert. More than a year had gone by—the concert was scheduled for the late fall of 1938. After trying to locate him Oertle had to tell Law that he couldn't get Johnson for the concert. He'd been murdered sometime during the summer.

The little that we know about Robert's death may be all we'll ever know. It wasn't important if a young black man died in Mississippi, so there isn't anything in newspaper files, and there's nothing on the death certificate. His brother, Red Johnson, died in Banks Quarters—another row of shacks in the delta south of Robinsonville—in the 1960's. Dick Waterman, one of the group of men who found Son House, was told that he was killed after a dance in Greenwood. He'd spent most of the evening with one girl, then he'd left with somebody else. The girl he'd been with at the dance followed them and stabbed him to death in bed with the other girl. Son House had heard that he was dead, but it was hard to tell how he'd died.

"... The next word we heard was from his mother, who told us he was dead. We never did get the straight of it. We first heard that he got stabbed to death. Next, a woman poisoned him, and then we heard something else. I can't remember what it was now, but it was three different things. Never did just get the straight of it. . ."

Shines remembers that the other thing they heard was that Robert was killed with "black arts," something that's sometimes said about any of the blues men who die young, and this story is told at least as often as the other stories about his death.

Son adds again the thing they always said about Robert, "... Close as I can get to it, he was about twenty-three or four. Very young."

Even if we knew more about Robert Johnson's life there still isn't much to say about twenty-two or three—or even twenty-six years. Something only begun, half started. And there isn't much more music. Twenty-nine blues. But there is the feeling that it's enough. We don't have much else, but we do have the artist that was Robert Johnson. With many singers, some of them very popular, there were only a few melodies—with some only one or two—a small vocabulary of blues ideas, and despite their two or three hundred recordings—Lonnie Johnson had done more than one hundred twenty released songs before Robert even started recording—they didn't give us as much—they didn't open themselves out as much as Robert did in his five short sessions. He used the same melody in more than one blues, he used some of the same guitar figures and accompaniments, he even took some of the songs and the styles from other blues records, but there was a wholeness to what he did. Everything is there. He wasn't trying to entertain anybody, he was singing about his own torments, his pain, his joy, and even when he did something that wasn't so intense, something less close to the surface of the skin, it seemed to be part of the total expression that is his blues.

The most important influence on his playing was certainly Son House. Muddy Waters, who was completely dominated by Johnson's recordings in the late thirties, learned the technique from Son, who had taught the same things to Robert several years before. It was Robert's style that excited Muddy—he was still working as a field hand outside of Clarksdale—but he learned it from Son House. When he did his first recordings for the Library of Congress in 1941 he told Alan Lomax that he'd never seen Robert, though he'd heard his recordings. Son had built his own style out of the rhythms of the field holler and the harsh emotionalism of Mississippi gospel song. Son wasn't a strong writer of blues texts, but he brought everything in him to his blues—without any withholding —and he shaped each of the blues to its accompaniment until the words and the music were one whole expression—and the guitar seemed to say the words and his voice seemed to sing with the stinging burr of the metal slide he used on his finger. His bottleneck playing—and this is what he gave to Robert—was in what they call in Mississippi "cross Spanish" tuning, e - b - e' - g$^{\#}$ - b' - e''. It makes an open E chord when all the strings are strummed at once, but it is almost never strummed. The lower strings are used as a kind of drone accompaniment, the thumb alternating on the e and the b strings to outline the basic harmony. The tonic chord that he uses is often played high up on the neck—with the first finger of the left hand pressing the top string on the seventh fret, the second finger of the left hand pressing the second string on the eighth fret. It's this that gives his music, and Robert's, some of its high sibilance.

What did Robert use for a bottleneck? Nobody has been able to remember. Son uses a metal slide on his third finger, Muddy, who learned from him, a broad, flat metal ring. But Muddy remembers that in the early days they used a real bottleneck, broken off the top of the bottle and then held in a flame until the edges were smooth. Furry Lewis uses a bottleneck sometimes in Memphis, but most of the time he uses a metal ring, like Muddy now. If you try to heat a bottle in a fire to get it smooth, as Muddy says, you won't get much smoothing out of it—since the melting point of glass is considerably higher than a wood fire. Maybe Muddy means the fires that they used to have in back country blacksmith shops—charcoal stoked and fired with a bellows. Furry smoothed the edge of his with a file. Johnny Shines, who is also a great slide player, uses the usual short length of metal tubing. On some of Robert's songs, when he is driven with the emotions of what he is singing—like *Preachin' Blues*—you can hear the clank of the slide against the frets, so he probably was using a bottleneck, which gets in the way of the guitar neck more than the smaller metal slide.

Robert's sources were broader than the instrumental techniques he learned from Son—Son's friend Willie Brown was an even better guitarist, and Robert must have learned some things from him—and from Charley Patton, the most dominating of all the singers of Son's generation. But there doesn't seem to be much from Patton—almost nothing. Only a slide guitar figure from one of Patton's pieces, *When Your Way Gets Dark*, that Robert used in *Come On In My Kitchen*. Unless the title itself left its shadow on the first line of Robert's *Stones In My Passway*, "I got stones in my passway and my way is dark as night." And since he was younger—sixteen or seventeen when the forty-two year old Patton made his first records—he listened to the phonograph—his musical horizon steadily being broadened by the recordings that were scattered everywhere, even through the small clusters of levee shacks. He heard all of it, and some of it left its traces in the sound of his blues. Some of what he recorded is openly derivative—the two Lonnie Johnson imitations, *Malted Milk* and *Drunken Hearted Man*, even use some of Lonnie's unique guitar phrases—but he was so open to influences that it's more surprising that what he recorded has such an internal unity. His music was completely his expression, and if it included a cursory look at someone else's style that was also a part of his own absorptions.

But even when he took something he changed it. One of the clearest examples of how he changed whatever he touched is the reworking of Son's *Preaching Blues*, described in the book *The Bluesmen*.

". . . In Son House's *Preaching Blues,* which he taught to Robert, most of the eleven verses, even though they reflected Son's inability to keep the secular and the religious sides of his life separated, were derived from other recordings, they were confused in their imagery, and there was little continuity in their develop-

ment. But one of the verses reflected a more direct meeting with the emotional realities.

> *Now, I met the blues this morning walking just like a man.*
> *Umh—walking just like a man.*
> *I said, "Good Morning, blues, now give me your right hand."*

It was this verse, the most immediate, that Robert chose to use first in his later recording, and he followed it with his own second verse that expressed even more vividly the painful intensity of the moment.

> *And the blues grabbed mama child, tore it all upside down.*
> *Blues grabbed mama child, and they tore me all upside down.*
> *Travel on, poor Bob, just can't turn you around. . .*

It was only after he had come so close to his own emotions that he could reach out his hand and touch the reflection of his own face that he went on to the generalized verses that took him a step back from the intensity of the experience, and his *Preachin' Blues* went on with,

> *The blues am a low down, stinkin' gyp.*
> *sp. (Preach 'em now.)*
> *Umh—am a low down stickin' gyp.*
> *You ain't never had 'em, hope you never will.*
>
> *Well the blues am a achin' old heart disease,*
> *sp. (do it now, you goin' do it?)*
> *But the blues am a low down achin' heart disease.*
> *Like consumption, killin' me by degrees. . ."*

The things in Robert's blues aren't that much different from the things in other blues—sex, its pleasure—women, their unfaithfullness—traveling, its painful solitude. But he opened all of it out, he had the sense of the immediacy of the experience in it. It wasn't just a girl—it was Thelma, who lived in East Monroe, Arkansas, or Betty Mae, the girl he said he was going to marry, the girl in Friars Point,

> *I ain't going to state no color, but her front teeth crowned with gold,*
> *I ain't going to state no color, but her front teeth is crowned with gold,*
> *She got a mortgage on my body now, lien on my soul.*

They have a reality, they're real women, not the standard woman figure who turns up in blues after blues as an almost meaningless symbol of infidelity. With Robert everything has its own poignant meaning. In his blues the woman must have been the one he was with the night before, or somebody he'd spent some days with in the weeks before he recorded. They had names, and they lived in towns he went through. In *Phonograph Blues* it's Beatrice, Thelma in *Dust My Broom*, Bernice in *Walkin' Blues*, Ida Belle in *Last Fair Deal Gone Down*, Betty Mae in *Honeymoon Blues*.

> *Betty Mae, you is my heartstrings, you is my destiny,*
> *Betty Mae, you is my heartstrings, you is my destiny,*
> *And you rolled across my mind, baby, each and every day . . .*
>
> *Some day I will return with my marriage license in my hand,*
> *Some day I will return, uumh, with a marriage license in my hand.*
> *I'm gonna take you for a honeymoon in some long, long distant land.*

Or Willie Mae in the great blues love song, *Love In Vain.*

And I followed her to the station with her suitcase in my hand,
And I followed her to the station with her suitcase in my hand,
Well, it's hard to tell it's hard to tell when all your love's in vain,
All my love's in vain.

When the train rolled up to the station, I looked her in the eye,
When the train rolled up to the station, and I looked her in the eye.
Well, I was lonesome, I felt so lonesome, and I could not help but cry.
All my love's in vain.

When the train, it left the station, there was two lights on behind.
When the train, it left the station, there was two lights on behind.
Well, the blue light was my blues, and the red light was my mind.
All my love's in vain.

Uumh, Willie Mae,
Uumh, Willie Mae,
Uumh, uumh, All my love's in vain.

The blues is almost driven with sexuality, and with Robert it was an even more intense obsession, even more of a wrench of pain or joy. Of the twenty-nine blues he did twenty of them are concerned with love and its physical torment. In ten of them it's the woman who's been unfaithful—or more than a third of the songs he recorded were about women who mistreated him. He was sullenly angry about it in the conventional verses of *32-20 Blues,* which he learned from a Skip James record—even forgetting to change one of the verses from "Wisconsin," the word Skip had used since he was recording in Grafton, Wisconsin, to "Hot Springs," close to where Robert was traveling.

Oh baby, where you stayed last night?
Oh baby, where you stayed last night?
You got your hair all tangled and you ain't talking right.

He used a rich vein of erotic imagery in *Terraplane Blues,* the first release from the material he recorded at the first group of sessions. His awareness that his woman had been unfaithful was expressed in a richly imagined sexual extravaganza—a wild association of sex and car parts that gets to the heart of some of the American sexual obsessions. There never has been anything quite like *Terraplane.*

And I feel so lonesome, you hear me when I moan,
And I feel so lonesome, you hear me when I moan,
Who's been drivin' my Terraplane for you since I been gone.

I said I'd flash your lights, mama, your horn won't even blow,
(Spoken: Something wrong with the battery down in this machine.)
I even flashed my lights, mama, this horn won't even blow,
There's a short in this connection, uumh well, babe, it's way down below.

I'm gonna hoist your hood, mama, I'm bound to check your oil,
I'm gonna hoist your hood, mama, I'm bound to check your oil,
I've got a woman that I'm loving, way down in Arkansas.

20

Now you know the coils ain't even buzzin', little generator won't get that
spark,
All in a bad condition, you gotta have these batteries charged,
I'm cryin' please, please don't do me wrong,
Who's been driving my Terraplane now for you since I've been gone . . .

His *Dead Shrimp Blues* was structured like *Terraplane*, but its imagery was centered around fishing, and it didn't have the effect of his automobile.

Johnson's blues have much in them that's difficult to fully comprehend. Certainly there isn't any way to catch the full emotional implications of everything that he's saying. It isn't his blackness—it's his localness. If you didn't grow up on a cotton plantation in north-central Mississippi you can't know the language of Mississippi farm life. Sometimes listening to a Chicago bluesman who isn't from Mississippi doing one of Robert's songs I get the feeling that he's at the same emotional distance from it as I am. It's possible to hunt down the terms—to find out what the word means—but the naturalness of it as language—the sense of it as a man's voice—this is the hardest to hear, without knowing the man's language as well as he knows it himself.

Through all of this, through all of the blues about trains and busses and women he loved and lost, or who hurt him, or slept with him, there is the same raw openness to what is happening to him. It was in his voice. He could sing in different styles, from a rough imitation of Son House to the high falsetto of Kokomo Arnold, but his own voice was as open, as unguarded. It's one of the most emotional points of his music, the sheer sound of his voice in its almost helpless youngness. And his obsessions are American obsessions—not just a Mississippi field hand's. The American self-image—for somebody under twenty—is the loner drifting down the road, leaving a girl, coming to a new girl, feeling lonely, feeling young, feeling horny, feeling gray and alone in the mornings. This is Robert's music—and this is part of why his music lives so strongly nearly forty years after he recorded it. The greatest of his songs have not only the rich identity of their Mississippi background, but also a total and immediate feeling of communication as song and expression—without need for explanation or terms. *Come On In My Kitchen* is one of the most beautiful songs of longing and sexual desire that anyone has ever written.

The woman I love took from my best friend,
Some joker got lucky, stole her back again,
You better come on in my kitchen, it's going to be rainin' outdoors . . .

When a woman gets in trouble, everybody throws her down,
Looking for her good friend, none can be found,
You better come on in my kitchen, it's going to be rainin' outdoors.

And the time's comin', it's goin' be so,
You can't make the winter, babe, just try long so,
You better come on in my kitchen, it's going to be rainin' outdoors.

As the recordings were released—they came out on the ARC, Vocalion and Conqueror labels in the late 1930's—it was the guitar style that most influenced other bluesmen. As a guitarist he almost completely turned the blues around. His tightening of the rhythmic line was the basis for the instrumental blues scene that followed him in Chicago—letting the upper strings play a free melodic part but using the thumb for a hard rhythm in the lower strings that was almost like a drum part. When Muddy Waters started his first bands in Chicago six or seven years later all he had to do was have the bass player and the drummer pick up on the bass part of Robert's style, and let the harmonica and the lead guitar pick up on the treble. Elmore James took less from Robert, but in his various versions of *Dust My Broom,* and all the other versions he did of the melody with different words, he caught the rough excitement of one part of Robert's style.

A last theme haunted Robert's music. It could have been as Shines said, that it was the black arts that killed him. He believed in the devil—or it seems from his blues that he believed in the devil—something is there. In six of his blues he mentions the devil, or the supernatural—voodoo, and it seemed to force its presence on some of his greatest music.

In *Me and The Devil Blues,* it's almost a friend.
Early this morning when you knocked upon my door,
Early this morning, umh, when you knocked upon my door,
And I said, "Hello, Satan, I believe it's time to go.

Me and the Devil was walking side by side,
Me and the Devil, uumh, was walking side by side,
I'm going to beat my woman until I get satisfied....

You may bury my body down by the highway side,
(Spoken: Baby, I don't care where you bury my body when I'm dead and gone.)
You may bury my body, uumh, down by the highway side,
So my old evil spirit can get a Greyhound bus and ride.

In the great *Hellhound On My Trail,* it's the whole force of evil that keeps following after him.

I got to keep moving, I got to keep moving, blues falling down like hail, blues falling down like hail.
Uumh—, blues falling down like hail, blues falling down like hail.
And the day keeps on 'minding me there's a hellhound on my trail, hellhound on my trail, hellhound on my trail....

You sprinkled hot foot powder all around my door, all around my door, all around my door.
You sprinkled hot foot powder all around your daddy's door,
It keeps me with a rambling mind, rider, every old place I go, every old place I go.

I can tell the wind is rising, the leaves trembling on the trees, trembling on the trees.
I can tell the wind is rising, leaves trembling on the trees, uumh.
All I need my sweet little woman to keep my company, uumh, my company.

It's there as a theme, as so many things of his life became the themes of his music. Which of the themes *was* his life? All of them, and in that is the greatness of what he created.

22

THE TRANSCRIPTIONS

In general I've tried to notate Robert Johnson's blues as closely as possible from the recordings he made of them, but certainly he altered all of the songs in each performance, and over the months or weeks he probably played and sang most of them pretty much as he felt. Some, like *Come On In My Kitchen,* probably had the same guitar accompaniment, some of the others probably used different tunings or even melodies. The most consistent alteration I've made has been in the key of the recording. Since he was working alone with a guitar he didn't have to concern himself with concert pitch, so many of the songs are sung in keys that are awkward for the guitar, unless he was using a capo, which would be unusual for a Mississippi musician from this period. Several were sung in concert Bb, several in B, two in concert F#. I have tried to transpose all of them to more natural keys for a blues guitarist, often A or E, or to G. He seems to be usually tuned a little sharp, which gives his accompaniments some of their brilliant clarity. In doing this I haven't tried to make transpositions to open guitar tunings, especially since it's often difficult to tell exactly how the guitar is tuned. An example of how complicated this can become is *Walkin' Blues,* which he sang in concert B, but the guitar is tuned to open G. Transposing the song down to G lowered it too much, and lost the feeling of the performance, but to leave it in B gave it a sense of harmonic complexity that was misleading, so I took it up to concert C, with the note that the guitar accompaniment should be raised with retuning or a capo.

I haven't transcribed the guitar introductions, since these generally followed a consistent pattern and seem loosely interchangeable from song to song. I have however, transcribed one introduction for piano in the key of A.

An introduction similar to those found in most of Robert Johnson's blues:

It is clear, in listening to all of the songs, that there were certain rhythm patterns that were consistent in Robert Johnson's style, and I've tried to follow them as closely as possible. Some of the accompaniments are built on triplets, or rhythms in 8ths, and there is often even a feeling that the voice and the guitar are in two different rhythmic modes, though the contrasts are so subtle that it's almost impossible to notate them. But despite these complexities I've felt that he was generally working within the usual blues framework of a three line verse unit, with a four beat measure as the base rhythm; so I've worked in this framework and the variations within this pattern still have been placed in an overall 4/4, with extended phrases or freer measures to clarify the differences. Some songs, of course, like *Love In Vain,* aren't standard blues, and they haven't been transcribed in this way.

Despite a great deal that has been written on the blues scale there is still no agreement as to how much of the difference between the blues scale and the European diatonic scale can be traced to clear scale modes, and how much is a looser response of the Afro-American melody to the European instruments that were generally used for accompaniment. Johnson was a sophisticated singer, who was influenced by many different sources; so his own use of a blues scale is considerably freer than the limited scales that an older singer like Charley Patton used. There is, however, a fairly consistent ambiguity in the third and the seventh of the scales—as well as occasional other tones in some of the songs—and I've tried to indicate the alteration he's made from standard pitch by marking the note with either a(+) or a(−). To get a sense of how the note should sound play the tone together with either the note a half step above or the note a half step below. On the piano for a G note marked with a (−), play the G together with the F$^\#$ directly below it, and let the G ring a little longer than the two notes together. Certainly there are surviving elements of older pentatonic or gapped-scaled melodies in Johnson's blues, but since the method of notation used is European and diatonic these figures can only be sensed on the written page.

I've included chords for the songs, but these have only a general use. If a guitarist is in open tuning and he slides up the neck of the guitar five frets he will have gone from a tonic to a subdominant harmony, and if he's in the key of G, then the progression can be marked from G to C. If it's played in any other way, however, it won't sound the same. Someone interested in copying the guitar accompaniments should work from the guitar tablature arrangements that Stefan Grossman has done for his excellent series of books on blues guitar.

For a blues artist, generally, and especially for an artist as complex and unique as Robert Johnson, a transcription can give only a partial feeling of the music, so the best way to use these transcriptions is with the recordings themselves. The transcriptions help to clarify what he has created, they make it possible to look at rhythmic patterns and at complexities of the text. They can help to show everything about the songs except their greatness, and that's on the recordings. But with the transcriptions it does become possible to understand the greatness more completely.

24

THE FIRST SESSION

Kindhearted Woman Blues

Recorded San Antonio, Monday, November 23, 1936
Matrix number SA-2580-1, 2
Original issue ARC 7-30-56, Vocalion 03416
Take 1 is reissued on Columbia lp 62456, take 2 on C30034

Key of the original recording B, transposed to A.

I love my baby, my baby don't love me,
I love my baby, uumh, my baby don't love me,
I really love that woman, can't stand to leave her be.

And there ain't but the one thing makes Mister Johnson dream,
I swear by how you treat me, baby, I begin to think,
Oh babe, my life don't be the same,
You breaks my heart when you calls Mister So and So's name.

26

She's a kindhearted woman, she studies evil all the time,
She's a kindhearted woman, she studies evil all the time,
You have to kill me just to have it on your mind.

The first three verses of the two takes are very similar, but in the first take the line *You breaks my heart when you calls Mister So and So's name* is followed by one of the few instrumental choruses that Johnson recorded, before going on to the final verse. In the second take there is no instrumental and there is an added verse.

Some day, some day, I will shake your hand goodbye
Some day, some day, I will shake your hand goodbye
I can't give you any more of my loving, 'cause I just ain't satisfied.

Muddy Waters did a version of the song early in his career, in 1948, with the text and melody very close to the original, but the rhythm more regular and a bass added. His version is available on Chess lp 1511. The form of the song is loosely a standard 12 bar blues, but there is anticipation of the harmonic changes that shortens the measure length between the vocal phrases. The last two lines of the middle verse (from *Oh babe, my life . . .*) are sung in falsetto. This is a semi-recited verse with the rhythm suspended for the first two lines.

I Believe I'll Dust My Broom

Recorded San Antonio, Monday, November 23, 1936
Matrix number SA-2581-1
Original issue ARC 7-04-81, Vocalion 03475, Conqueror 8871
Reissued on Columbia lp C30034

Key of original recording E.

I'm goin' get up in the morn - ing
I be-lieve I'll dust my broom
I'm goin' get up in the morn - ing
I be - lieve I'll dust my broom
girl friend, the black man you been lov - in'
girl friend, can get my room.
I'm goin'

I'm gonna write a letter, telephone every town I know,
I'm gonna write a letter, telephone every town I know.
If I can't find her in West Helena, she must be in East Monroe, I know.

28

I don't want no woman wants every downtown man she meets,
I don't want no woman wants every downtown man she meets,
She's a no good (pony?) they shouldn't 'low her on the streets.

I believe, I believe I'll go back home.
I believe, I believe I'll go back home.
You can mistreat me here, babe, but you can't when I go home.

And I'm gettin' up in the morning, I believe I'll dust my broom,
I'm gettin' up in the morning, I believe I'll dust my broom,
Girl friend, the black man you been lovin', girl friend, can get my room.

I'm gonna call up China, see is my good girl over there,
I'm gonna call up China, see is my good girl over there,
I can't find her on Philippines Islands, she must be in Ethiopia somewhere.

The prefix SA in the matrix number indicated San Antonio, and it was because of this that the first place to begin looking for him was in the San Antonio black neighborhoods. Both West Helena and East Monroe are in Arkansas, and West Helena was described earlier.

East Monroe is about 60 miles north west of West Helena, west on route 49, then north east on route 79. Elmore James' first recording, for the Trumpet label in Jackson, Mississippi, in 1952, was a version of the song, with Sonny Boy Williamson playing harmonica and Odie Johnson, bass. He recorded it also as *Dust My Blues*, and used the melody for several of his own songs. It was so closely identified with him that he named his group the *Broomdusters*. His cousin and second guitarist, Homesick James Williamson, recorded it in December, 1965 for Vanguard lp VRS 8217, and Maxwell Street Jimmy Davis recorded it on Electra lp EKL 303. James usually played it as a bottleneck, or slide, piece, but Johnson's original accompaniment is finger picked. It is particularly interesting as one of the first recorded examples of what was to become the classic Chicago shuffle beat, with the repeated groups of triplets in the treble strings of the guitar the rhythmic figure that was to become a basic pattern for blues pianists like Otis Spann.

Sweet Home Chicago

Recorded San Antonio, Monday, November 23, 1936
Matrix number SA-2582-1
Original issue Vocalion 03601
Reissued on Columbia lp C30034

The confusion of California for Illinois suggests that Johnson hadn't traveled to Chicago before he recorded the song. Little Junior Parker recorded a song with the same title for Duke label in 1958, but the songs may not be similar. A source for the song is probably Kokomo Arnold's popular *Old Original Kokomo Blues*, recorded in 1934 for Decca. There are many similarities in the melodic line, particularly the phrase *sweet home Chicago*. Johnson may also have taken some of his use of sudden falsetto notes from Arnold, though this was a characteristic of some local Mississippi styles.

Key of original recording F, transposed to G.

(In his singing of this blues he repeats the first verse, but since it's the only blues he sings this way it was probably not intentional.)

Now two and two is four, four and two is six,
You gonna keep on monkeying 'round with your friends, boy,
    You gonna get your business thrown out on the street,

But I'm cryin', baby, honey, don't you want to go,
Back to the land of California, to my sweet home Chicago.

Now six and two is eight, eight and two is ten,
Friends, boy, she trick you one time, she sure goin' do it again,
I'm cryin' hey, baby, don't you want to go,
To the land of California, to my sweet home Chicago.

I'm going to California, (?)
Somebody will tell me that you need my help someday,
Cryin' hey hey, baby, don't you want to go,
To the land of California, to my sweet home Chicago.

Ramblin' On My Mind

Recorded San Antonio, Monday, November 23, 1936
Matrix number SA-2583-1, 2
Original issue ARC 7-05-81, Vocalion 03419
Reissued on Columbia lp 62455 and C30034, both lps using take 2

This melody is almost identical with *When You Got A Good Friend*, the next piece he recorded. Both of them use a shuffle accompaniment with many similarities to the guitar part he used for *I Believe I'll Dust My Broom*. Johnny Shines did a brilliant version of the song, with the title *Ramblin'* for Chicago's JOB label in 1952. He later remembered that it was something that came to him almost spontaneously when he got into the recording studio. The original release was JOB 116. Big Joe Williams also did a version of it on his Milestone lp 3001 in the summer of 1964.

Key of original recording F#, transposed to G.

32

I got mean things, I got mean things all on my mind,
Little girl, little girl, I got mean things all on my mind,
Hate to leave you here, babe, but you treat me so unkind.

Runnin' down to the station, catch the first mail train I see,
　　Spoken: *I think I hear it coming now.*
Runnin' down to the station, catch that old first mail train I see.
I got the blues 'bout Miss So and So, and the child got the blues about me.

And I'm leavin' this morning with my arms folded up and cryin',
And I'm leavin' this morning with my arms folded up and cryin',
I hate to leave my baby, but she treats me so unkind.

I got mean things, I got mean things on my mind,
I got mean things, I got mean things all on my mind,
I got to leave my baby, but she treats me so unkind.

When You Got A Good Friend

Recorded San Antonio, Monday, November 23, 1936
Matrix number SA-2584-1
Original issue Columbia lp 62456. This was unissued prior to its appearance on lp.

The subdominant phrase—the second line—has been extended in the first verse so there is an extra measure, although it is clearly in the 12 bar blues pattern.

Key of original recording F$^\#$, transposed to G.

When you got a good friend that will stay right by your side, _____ When you got a good friend that will stay right by your side, Give her all (of) your spare time love and treat her right. I mis-

I mistreated my babe, and I can't see no reason why,
I mistreated my babe, but I can't see no reason why,
Everytime I think about it I just wring my hands and cry.

Wonder could I bear to apologize, or would she sympathize with me,
Uumh, would she sympathize with me,
She's a brownskin woman, just as sweet as a girl friend can be.

Uumh, babe, I may be right or wrong.
Babe, tell me your feeling, uumh, I may be right or wrong.
Watch your close friend, baby, then your enemies can't do you no harm.

When you got a good friend that will stay right by your side,
When you got a good friend that will stay right by your side,
Give her all your spare time, love and treat her right.

34

WELCOME
CHURCH of CHRIST
SO. BISCOE   RICHMOND HILL
HELENA   WEST HELENA

Come On In My Kitchen

Recorded San Antonio, November 23, 1936
Matrix number SA-2585-1
Original issue ARC 7-07-57, Vocalion 03563
Reissued on Columbia lp 62456

Key of original recording B♭, transposed to A.

The woman I love, took from my best friend,
Some joker got lucky, stole her back again,
You better come on in my kitchen, it's going to be rainin' outdoors.

36

Boys, she's gone, I know she won't come back,
I taken the last nickel out of her (nation?) sack,
You better come on in my kitchen, it's going to be rainin' outdoors.

Spoken: *Oh, can't you hear that wind howlin', oh, can't you hear that wind
howling.*
You better come on in my kitchen, it's going to be rainin' outdoors.

When a woman gets in trouble, everybody throws her down,
Looking for her good friend, none can be found,
You better come on in my kitchen, it's going to be rainin' outdoors.

And the time's comin', it's goin' be so,
You can't make the winter, babe, just try long so,
You better come on in my kitchen, it's going to be rainin' outdoors.

For this song he retuned the guitar to an open D, and for the first time used a
slide in the guitar accompaniment. The song was played with considerable unison between the guitar and voice in a very slow tempo. In its mood, in the
opening lines, it has some of the feeling of Blind Willie Johnson's *Dark Was The
Night And Cold The Ground*, recorded for Columbia in 1927, which was also
hummed, with an accompaniment using a slide in unison with the voice.

In Johnson's accompaniment for this song there is no chord change. He plays
the rhythm on the bottom strings of the guitar and plays in unison with the
voice on the upper strings. Open D tuning is d-a-d'-f-a'-d".

37

Terraplane Blues

Recorded San Antonio, November 23, 1936
Matrix number SA 2586-1
Original issue ARC 7-03-56, Vocalion 03416
Reissued on Columbia lp 62456

For this piece he left the guitar in the same tuning, but it was raised a little, probably as he tuned again between takes. It's also played with a slide, as *Come On In My Kitchen*. With *Kindhearted Woman Blues* on the other side this was his first release, and many musicians still remember their excitement at hearing it the first time. He used the same melody and basic accompaniment for other blues, among them *Stones In My Passway*, and *Milkcow's Calf Blues*. The Terraplane was a 1930's car with considerable flash that was manufactured by the Hudson Motor Company. Big Joe Williams recorded a version of the song in 1964 on Milestone lp 3001, and Johnny Shines did a version on Vanguard lp VRS 9218. Shines, recording in December, 1965, modernized the title to *Dynaflow Blues*.

Key of original recording B, transposed to C.

And I feel so lone-some you hear me when I moan,—

— And I feel so lone - some

you hear me when I moan.——

Who's been driv - in' my Ter - ra - plane for you

since I been gone? I said I'd flash

Middle Section　　**C7**

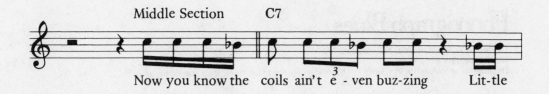

Now you know the　coils ain't e - ven buz-zing　　Lit-tle

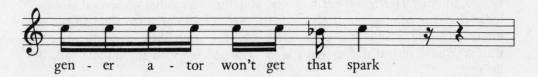

gen - er　a - tor　won't get　that spark

All　in a bad　con - di - tion you got - ta have

(falsetto)

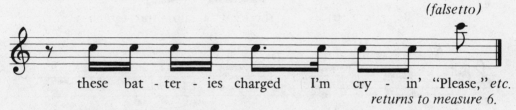

these bat - ter - ies charged　I'm　cry - in' "Please," *etc.*
returns to measure 6.

I said I'd flash your lights, mama, your horn won't even blow,
　　Spoken: *Something wrong with the battery down in this machine.*
I even flashed my lights, mama, this horn won't even blow,
There's a short in this connection, uumh well, babe, it's way down below.

I'm gonna hoist your hood, mama, I'm bound to check your oil,
I'm gonna hoist your hood, mama, I'm bound to check your oil,
I've got a woman that I'm loving, way down in Arkansas.

Now you know the coils ain't even buzzin', little generator won't get that spark,
All in a bad condition, you gotta have these batteries charged,
I'm cryin' please, please don't do me wrong,
Who's been driving my Terraplane now for you since I've been gone.

Mister highway man, please don't block the road,
Uumh, please don't block the road,
'Cause she's reachin' a cold one hundred, and I'm booked and I gotta go.

Uumh, uumh,
Uumh, you hear me weep and moan,
Who's been drivin' my Terraplane now for you since I've been gone.

I'm goin' to get deep down in this connection, keep on tangling with your wires,
I'm goin' to get deep down in this connection, uumh, keep on tangling with these
　　wires,
And when I mash down on your starter, and your spark plug will give me power.

39

Phonograph Blues

Recorded in San Antonio, November 23, 1936
Matrix number SA-2587-
Original issue Columbia lp C30034. This was unissued prior to its appearance on lp.

He went back to the original tuning for this, using an accompaniment style similar to *Kind Hearted Woman Blues*, and there are other structural and melodic elements common to both of them, even a four line verse as a half-spoken interlude in the middle of the piece. He used the same girl's name, Beatrice, in *Walkin' Blues*, recorded four days later. The accent is on the middle syllable, Be-á-trice.

Key of original recording B, transposed to A.

Beatrice, I love my phonograph, but you have broke my winding chain,
Beatrice, I love my phonograph, uumh, and you have broke my winding chain,
And you taken my loving and give it to your other man.

Now we played it on the sofa, now we played it 'side the wall,
My needles have got rusty, they will not play at all.
We played it on the sofa and we played it 'side the wall,
But my needles have got rusty and will not play at all.

Beatrice, now I'm going crazy, baby I will lose my mind,
And I'm going crazy, uumh, honey, I will lose my mind,
Won't you bring your clothes back home and try me one more time.

She got a phonograph, and it won't say a lonesome word,
She got a phonograph, and it won't say a lonesome word,
What evil have I done, or what evil have the poor girl heard?

THE SECOND AND THIRD SESSIONS

West Helena

32-20 Blues

Recorded in San Antonio, Thursday, November 26, 1936
Matrix number SA-2616-1
Original issue ARC 7-04-60, Vocalion 03445
Reissued on Columbia lp 62456

This is Robert's version of the *22-20 Blues* that Skip James recorded in February, 1931, in Grafton, Wisconsin. It was released on both Paramount and the Champion labels. Johnson's version changes the reference to Wisconsin in every verse but the third from last, when he forgets and uses Skip's original text instead of his own adaptation that changed the location to Hot Springs, Arkansas. Skip remembers that this was a song he made up in the studio when he was asked to do a song like the *44* and *38* blues that were popular during the period, and the text is largely derivative. This take was the only recording Robert did at this session.

Key of original recording and transcription A.

And if she gets unruly, thinks she don't want me,
If she gets unruly and thinks she don't want me,
Take my 32-20 and I can cut her half in two.

She's got a .38 Special, but I believe it's most too light,
She's got a .38 Special, but I believe it's most too light,
I've got a 32-20, got to make the cats all right.

If I send for my baby, man, and she don't come,
If I send for my baby, man, and she don't come,
All the doctors in Hot Springs sure can't help her none.

I'm gonna shoot my pistol, gonna shoot my girl and gone,
I'm gonna shoot my pistol, gotta shoot my girl and gone,
You made me love you, now your man have gone.

Oh baby, where you stayed last night?
Oh baby, where you stayed last night?
You got the hair all tangled, and you ain't talking right.

Got a .38 Special boys, it do very well,
Got a .38 Special boys, it do very well.
I got a 32-20 now, and it's a burning . . . (verse unfinished)

If I send for my baby, man, and she don't come,
If I send for my baby, man, and she don't come,
All the doctors in Wisconsin sure can't help her none.

Hey hey, baby, where you stayed last . . .
Hey hey, baby, where you stayed last night?
You didn't come home until the sun was shining bright.

Uumh, boy, I just can't take my rest,
Uumh, boy, I just can't take my rest,
With this 32-20 laying up and down my breast.

They're Red Hot

Recorded San Antonio, Friday, November 27, 1936
Matrix number SA-2627
Original issue ARC 7-07-57, Vocalion 03563
Reissued on Columbia lp C30034

Key of original recording and transcription C.

(For each verse the first two lines and the last line are the same as in the first verse, and the only new lines are the breaks at lines three and four.)

She got two for a nickel, got four for a dime,
Would sell you more, but they ain't none of mine.

I got a letter from a girl in the room,
Now she got something good she got to bring home soon.

 Spoken: *It's too hot, boys.*
The billy goat backed in the bumble bee's nest,
Ever since that he can't take his rest.

 Spoken: *Man, you don't mess around with hot tamales, you might be dead if you mess around with them hot tamales.*
(this break is almost unintelligible, the second line ending with . . . hard to beat.)

You know grandma loves them and grandpa too,
And I wonder what in the world we children gonna do.

Me and my babe bought a V-8 Ford,
Well, we bought that thing all on the running board.

You know the monkey and the baboon playing in the grass,
Well, the monkey said to the baboon, ("Good luck, yes?")

I got a girl say she's long and tall,
Now she sleeps in the kitchen with her feets in the hall.

 The composer credited for this song is Robert's brother, "Red" Johnson. The melody and chord pattern were widely known and recorded under many different titles, probably the best known was some variation of *Take Your Fingers Off It*. Big Bill Broonzy recorded it for Bluebird in the fall of 1935 as *Take Your Hands Off Her*. The first vocal break text, *I got a girl say she's long and tall / she sleeps in the kitchen, well, her head's in the hall*, was usually included in other versions. This was the only example of a southern medicine show "hokum" song that Robert recorded.

47

Dead Shrimp Blues

Recorded San Antonio, November 27, 1936
Matrix number SA-2628-2
Original issue ARC 7-05-81, Vocalion 03475, Conqueror 8871
Reissued on Columbia lp C30034

This is very closely related, in melody and accompaniment to *Kind Hearted Woman Blues*.

Key of original recording B♭, transposed to A.

I got dead shrimps, baby, someone is fishing in my pond,
I got dead shrimps, baby, uumh, someone's fishing in my pond,
I've tried my best bait, baby, and I can't do that no more.

Everything I do, baby, you got your mouth stuck out,
    Hole where I used to fish, you got me posted out.
Everything that I do, you got your mouth stuck out,
    At the hole where I used to fish, baby, you got me posted out.

I got dead shrimps, yeah, someone's fishing in my pond,
I got dead shrimps, yeah, someone's fishing in my pond,
Catching my goggle-eyed perches and they barbecuing the bones.

Now you taken my shrimps, baby, you know you turned me down,
    I couldn't do nothing until I got myself unwound.
You taken my shrimps, uumh, know you turned me down,
    Baby, can't do nothing until I get myself unwound.

Crossroad Blues

Recorded San Antonio, November 27, 1936
Matrix number SA-2629-1
Original issue ARC 7-05-81, Vocalion 03519
Reissued as *Crossroad Blues* on Columbia lp 62456

Key of original recording B, transposed to C.

I went to the cross - road fell down on my knee.

went to the cross - road fell down on my knee.

Asked the Lord a - bove have mer - cy,

save poor Bob if you please. umh

Uumh, standing at the crossroad, I tried to flag a ride.
Standing at the crossroad, I tried to flag a ride.
Didn't nobody seem to know me, everybody pass me by.

Uumh, the sun going down, boy, dark gonna catch me here.
Uumh, dark gonna catch me here.
I haven't got no loving sweet woman that loves and feels my care.

You can run, you can run, tell my friend, poor Willie Brown,
You can run, tell my friend, poor Willie Brown,
Lord, that I'm standing at the crossroad, babe, I believe I'm sinking down.

This is ambiguous rhythmically, with a basic 4/4 pulse, but an accompaniment with the feel of doubled 8th note values, putting it in 8/8. The melody and guitar background are very close to his *Terraplane Blues*, after the first verse of *Terraplane*. He seems to be suggesting, with the line *Uumh, the sun going down, boy, dark gonna catch me here*, that he was in one of the parts of Mississippi where any black found on the roads at night could be arrested. The Willie Brown in the last verse has been thought to be the close friend of Son House, the Willie Brown who was doing a lot of singing with Son when Robert first began playing. There was, however, a younger Willie Brown who was also a blues singer from this area and recorded for the Library of Congress and it could have been him. It also, of course, could have been still another man named Willie Brown that Robert was singing about, and without Robert himself to tell who he meant there isn't any way to tell. Elmore James recorded a version of it in 1954 or 1955 for Flair Records in Chicago, with the title *Standing At The Crossroads*. He changed the text, however, so it lost any larger meaning that Johnson might have been suggesting, and it becomes a standard Chicago blues with the verses beginning,

People, I was standing at the crossroad with my head hung down and cryin. . . .
Well, I was looking for my baby and I know she's not around.
I worked hard for my baby and she treats me like a slave. . . .
Well, I'm standin' at the crossroads and my baby not around. . . .

James recorded it again in New York in 1962 for Enjoy Records, and Homesick James recorded it as *Crossroads* for USA label in Chicago the same year.

Walkin' Blues

Recorded San Antonio, November 27, 1936
Matrix number SA-2630-1
Original issue Vocalion 03601
Reissued as *Walking Blues* on Columbia lp 62456

Key of original recording B, transposed to C.

Lord, I feel like blowing my old lonesome horn,
Got up this morning my little Bernice was gone,
Lord, I feel like blowing my lonesome horn,
Well, I got up this morning, all I had was gone.

Well, leave this morning if I have to, oh, ride the blinds,
I feel mistreated and I don't mind dyin',
Leavin' this morning, I have to ride the blinds,
Babe, I've been mistreated, baby, and I don't mind dyin'.

Well, some people tell me that the worried blues ain't bad,
Worst old feeling I most ever had,
Some people tell me that these old worried old blues ain't bad,
It's the worst old feeling I most ever had.

She's got an Elgin movement from her head down to her toes,
Break in on a dollar most anywhere she goes,
Uumh, her head down to her toes,
    Spoken: *Oh, alright*
Lord, she break in on a dollar most everywhere she goes.

Walkin' Blues has so many things reminiscent of Son Houses' style that it's probably a song Robert learned from him. The rhythm—with the short rest before each vocal phrase—has the same work-gang phrasing that Son used in a number of his pieces. These songs were so closely linked to their work-gang roots that they still were phrased with that short pause left for what was probably an axe blow. Chopping songs recorded in southern prisons have this same characteristic form of a short vocal line—the axes lifting while the songster sings the phrase—then the sharp noise of the axes hitting the tree, all of it in a steady, slow rhythm that a strong work gang could keep up for hours. The accompaniment is a bare reiteration of the basic pulse, played in an open G tuning. Muddy Waters' earliest recording, the *Country Blues* that he did for the Library of Congress in Stovall, Mississippi, in the summer of 1941, is a rather nervous copy of *Walkin' Blues,* and he has continued to perform it over the years. Big Joe Williams also recorded a version of it on Milestone 3001. Open G tuning is d - g - d' - g' - b - d''.

Last Fair Deal Gone Down

Recorded in San Antonio, November 27, 1936
Matrix number SA-2631-1
Original issue ARC 7-04-60, Vocalion 03445
Reissued on Columbia lp 62456

The Gulfport Island Railroad ran north through Mississippi from the city of Gulfport, on the Gulf of Mexico. This four line verse form seems to be a more archaic blues form, found also in Texas in the widely known older Texas song *Red River Blues*. Like *Come On In My Kitchen* and *Preachin' Blues* this is in open tuning, and there is no chord change in the accompaniment.

Key of original recording and transcription A.

Please, Ida Belle, don't cry this time,
Ida Belle, don't cry this time,
If you cry about a nickel, you'll die 'bout a dime,
She will cry, put your money on mine.

I love the way you do,
I love the way you do,
I love the way you do, good lord,
On this Gulfport Island Road.

My captain's so mean on me,
My captain's so mean on me,
My captain's so mean on me, good lord,
On this Gulfport Island Road.

It's the last fair deal goin' down,
It's the last fair deal goin' down,
It's the last fair deal goin' down, good lord,
On this Gulfport Island Road.

I'm working my way back home,
I'm working my way back home,
I'm working my way back home, good lord,
On this Gulfport Island Road.

And that thing don't keep ringin' so soon,
That thing don't keep ringin' so soon,
And that thing don't keep ringin' so soon, good lord,
On that Gulf-and-port Island Road.

Preachin' Blues

Recorded San Antonio, November 27, 1936
Matrix number SA-2632-1, 2
Original issue Vocalion 04630
Reissued on Columbia lp 62456 and C30034. Both albums use take 1.

Key of original recording and transcription E.

I was up this morn-ing,   I got

blues   walk-ing like a man.___

I was up this morn - ing,

my blues walk-ing like a man.___

Well, the   blues___

give me your right hand.___   And the

And the blues fell, mama child, and they tore me all upside down,
Blues fell, mama child, and they tore me all upside down,
Travel on, poor Bob, just can't turn you 'round.

The blues is a low down stinkin' gyp,
Uumh, is a low down stinkin' gyp,
You ain't never had 'em, I hope you never will.

Well, the blues is a achin' old heart disease,
  Spoken: *Do it now, You gonna do it.*
The blues is a low down achin' heart disease,
Like consumption, killin' me by degrees.

Now if it starts a-rainin', oh drive, oh oh drive my blues,
Now if it starts a-rainin', I'm gonna drive my blues away,
Goin' to (Steeray?), stay out there all day.

 This is Robert's version of *Preachin' The Blues, Parts 1 and 2*, that Son House recorded for Paramount in Grafton, Wisconsin in the summer of 1930. His changes from Son's text have been discussed earlier. With *Preachin' Blues* the session that had begun with the hokum blues of *They're Red Hot* reached a point of emotional frenzy that he never reached again on record. The accompaniment, like *Come On In My Kitchen*, has no change in harmony, but is played as rhythmic bass and a melody pattern above it. The tuning is probably open D.

If I Had Possession Over Judgement Day

Recorded San Antonio, November 27, 1936
Matrix Number SA-2633-1
Original issue Columbia lp 62456. This was unissued prior to its appearance on lp.

This is another version of the Mississippi piece often known as *Rollin' and Tumblin,* though in many versions it is also known as *Brownsville Blues.* As *Rollin' and Tumblin'* it was recorded by a number of Chicago singers, among them Muddy Waters. It also sounds like a piece that Robert learned from Son House, and has the same melody and accompaniment as a blues he did the next year in Dallas, *Traveling Riverside Blues.* Son also used a verse beginning, *Had to fold my arms, and I slowly walked away* in his great blues *My Black Woman,* his line slightly different in the version he recorded for the Library of Congress, *You know, I fold my arms and I slowly walk away. . .* Both this and *Traveling Riverside Blues* are in open G tuning.

Key of original recording and transcription A.

If I had pos-ses-sion o-ver Judge-ment day—

— If I had pos-ses-sion

o-ver judge-ment day, _____ Lord, then

the lit - tle wom -an I'm lov - in' would - n t

have no right to pray._ And I

And I went to the mountain, just as far as my eyes could see,
And I went to the mountain, just as far as my eyes could see,
Some other man got my woman, and these lonesome blues got me.

And I rolled and I tumbled and I cried the whole night long,
And I rolled and I tumbled and I cried the whole night long,
Boy, I woke up this morning, my biscuit roller gone.

Had to fold my arms, and I slowly walked away,
    Spoken: *I didn't like the way she done.*
Had to fold my arms, and I slowly walked away.
I felt in my mind, your trouble gonna come some day.

Now run here, baby, sit down on my knee.
Now run here, baby, sit down on my knee.
I want to tell you all about the way they treated me.

THE FOURTH SESSION

Commerce, where he grew up

Stones In My Passway

Recorded Dallas, Saturday, June 19, 1937
Matrix number DAL-377-2
Original issue ARC 7-12-67, Vocalion 03723, Conqueror 8973
Reissued on Columbia lp 62456

This has the same melody and accompaniment as *Terraplane Blues* and *Milkcow's Calf Blues.*

Key of original recording and transcription A.

I got stones _____ in my pass - way

and my road seems dark as night. I got

stones___ in my pass-way and my road seems dark as night.___

I have pains in my heart they have tak-en my ap-pe-tite.

I have a bird___

I have a bird to whistle and I have a bird to sing.
Have a bird to whistle and I have a bird to sing,
I got a woman that I'm lovin', boy, but she don't mean a thing.

My enemies have betrayed me, have overtaken poor Bob at last,
My enemies have betrayed me, have overtaken poor Bob at last,
And there's one thing certain, they have stones all in my path.

Now you tryin' to take my life, and all my lovin' too,
You laid the passway for me, now what are you trying to do?
I'm cryin' please, please, let us be friends,
And when you hear me howling in my passway, rider, please open your door and
    let me in.

I got (three lane truck on?), boys, please don't block my road,
I got (three lane truck on?), boys, please don't block my road,
I been feelin' shamed by my rider, babe, I'm booked and I got to go.

I'm A Steady Rollin' Man

Recorded Dallas June 19, 1937
Matrix number DAL-378-1
Original issue ARC 7-12-67, Vocalion 03723, Conqueror 8973
Reissued on Columbia C30034

Key of original recording Bb, transposed to A.

I'm the man that rolls when icicles hanging on the tree,
I'm the man that rolls when icicles hanging on the tree,
And now you hear me howling, baby, uumh, down on my bended knee.

I'm a hard working man, have been for many years I know,
I'm a hard working man, have been for many long years I know,
And some cream puff's using my money, uumh, well, babe, but that'll never be
   no more.

You can't give your sweet woman everything she wants in one time,
Uumh, you can't give your sweet woman everything she wants in one time,
Well, boys, she gets rambling in her brain, uumh, some other man on her mind.

I'm a steady rolling man, I roll both night and day,
I am your steady rolling man and I roll both night and day,
Well, I don't have no sweet woman, uumh boys, to be rolling this a-way.

From Four Until Late

Recorded Dallas, June 19, 1937
Matrix number DAL-379-1
Original issue ARC 7-09-56, Vocalion 03623
Reissued on Columbia lp C30034 as *From Four Till Late*

The smoother, almost sentimental style of this blues would seem to place its source out of Mississippi, and the second verse does mention the distance from Memphis to Norfolk, Virginia. The piece could have come from one of the less intense areas of blues song in the eastern seaboard states, although the accompaniment is not like any of the guitar styles of that section.

Key of original recording and transcription C.

From four 'till late___ I was wring-in' my hands and cryin'_____ From four 'till late___ I was wring-in' my hands and cryin'. I be-lieve to my soul_ that your dad-dy's Gulf-port bound. From

From Memphis to Norfolk is a thirty-six hours' ride,
From Memphis to Norfolk is a thirty-six hours' ride,
A man is like a prisoner, and he's never satisfied.

A woman is like a dresser, some man's always ramblin' through its drawers,
A woman is like a dresser, some man's always ramblin' through its drawers,
It cause so many men to wear an apron overall.

From four 'til late she (give up?) a no good bunch and clown,
From four 'til late she (give up?) a no good bunch and clown,
Now she won't do nothing but tear a good man's reputation down.

When I leave this town I'm gonna bid you fare, farewell,
And when I leave this town I'm gonna bid you fare, farewell,
And when I return again you'll have a great long story to tell.

THE FIFTH SESSION

Hell Hound On My Trail

Recorded Dallas, Sunday, June 20, 1937
Matrix number DAL-394-2
Original issue ARC 7-09-56, Vocalion 03623
Reissued on Columbia lp 62456

Key of original recording and transcription E.

If today was Christmas Eve, if today was Christmas Eve, and tomorrow was
   Christmas Day,
If today was Christmas Eve, and tomorrow was Christmas Day,
   Spoken: *Oh, wouldn't we have a time, baby.*
All I would need my little sweet rider, just to pass the time away, uumh, to pass
   the time away.

You sprinkled hot foot powder all around my door, all around my door.
You sprinkled hot foot powder all around your daddy's door.
It keeps me with a rambling mind, rider, every old place I go, every old place I go.

I can tell the wind is rising, the leaves trembling on the trees, trembling on the trees.
I can tell the wind is rising, leaves trembling on the trees, uumh.
All I need my sweet little woman and to keep my company, uumh, my company.

   The form of *Hell Hound On My Trail* seems to be unique—there is no other
blues with the same melody and verse form. It is difficult to know exactly what
he meant by the *hell hound,* but the image of the hounds of hell, coming to seize
sinners, was used often in southern churches. The first and last verses are perhaps
the finest moments in all blues poetry. Big Joe Williams recorded the same song
in 1964 for his Milestone lp, but, like all of the other songs that he did at the
same time, this came after he'd heard a group of Johnson's blues played for him
by young blues enthusiasts.

Little Queen Of Spades

Recorded Dallas, June 20, 1937
Matrix number DAL-395-1, 2
Original issue Vocalion 04108
Reissued on Columbia lp C30034

Key of original recording and transcription A.

Well, I'm goin' get me a gambling woman if it's the last thing that I do,
Uumh, goin' get me a gambling woman if it's the last thing that I do,
A man don't need a woman, uumh fair brown, he got to give all his money to.

And everybody says she got a mojo, baby, you been using that stuff,
Uumh, everybody says she got a mojo, 'cause she been using that stuff,
She got her way trembling down, oh well, babe, and I mean it's most too tough.

Well, well, little girl says I am the king, fair brown, and you is the queen,
Uumh, says I'm the king, baby, and you is the queen,
Let's we put our heads together, uumh fair brown, then we can make our money
    green.

The *mojo* mentioned in the third verse is the same kind of charm that Muddy Waters refers to in *Got My Mojo Working.* It's used against someone else, either as a love charm, or to bring them bad luck—and the word often has more of a general meaning than a specific identity as a potion or charm. Musically the song is closely related to his *Phonograph Blues, Honeymoon Blues,* and *Dead Shrimp Blues.* Blind Lemon Jefferson also did a mojo blues, his *Low Down Mojo Blues* from 1928.

Malted Milk

Recorded Dallas, June 20, 1937
Matrix number DAL-396-1
Original issue ARC 7-10-65, Vocalion 03665, Conqueror 8944
Reissued on Columbia lp C30034

These two songs, *Malted Milk* and *Drunken Hearted Man,* have many elements of the style of Lonnie Johnson, including some of his distinctive guitar figures, and the kind of wistful seriousness of his voice. Lonnie Johnson had been making recordings with many different accompanists, often closer to a jazz feeling, but this is the older style of Lonnie's recordings of the late 1920's, something like the *Roaming Rambler Blues* or *Tin Can Alley Blues,* both done for OKeh label in 1927.

Key of original recording E♭, transposed to E.

Malted milk, malted milk keeps rushin' to my head,
Malted milk, malted milk keeps rushin' to my head,
And I have a funny, funny feelin' that I'm talking all out of my head.

Baby, fix me one more drink, and hug your daddy one more time,
Baby, fix me one more drink, and hug your daddy one more time,
Keep on studyin' my malted milk, mam, until I change my mind.

My doorknob keeps on turnin', it must be spooks around my bed,
My doorknob keeps on turnin', must be spooks around my bed,
I have a warm old feeling and the hair rising on my head.

Helena, where he lived in the thirties

Drunken-Hearted Man

Recorded Dallas, June 20, 1937
Matrix number DAL-397-1
Original issue Columbia la C30034. This was unissued prior to its appearance on lp.

Key of original recording E♭, transposed to E.

I'm a drunk en heart-ed man, my life seems so mi-ser-y.

I'm a poor drunk-en heart-ed man, my life seems so mi-ser-y.

And if I could on-ly change my way of liv-ing

it would mean so much to me. I been

I've been dogged and I've been driven, ever since I left my mother's home,
I've been dogged and I've been driven, ever since I left my mother's home,
And I can't see the reason why I can't leave these no good womens alone.

My poor father died and left me, and my mother done the best that she could,
My poor father died and left me, and my mother done the best that she could,
Every man love that game you call love, but it don't mean no man no good.

Now I'm the poor drunken hearted man, and sin was the cause of it all,
I'm a poor drunken hearted man, and sin was the cause of it all,
But the day that you get weak for no good woman, that's the day that you surely
   fall.

74

Me and the Devil Blues

Recorded Dallas, June 20, 1937
Matrix number DAL 398-1, 2
Original issue Vocalion 04108

Key of original recording B♭, transposed to A.

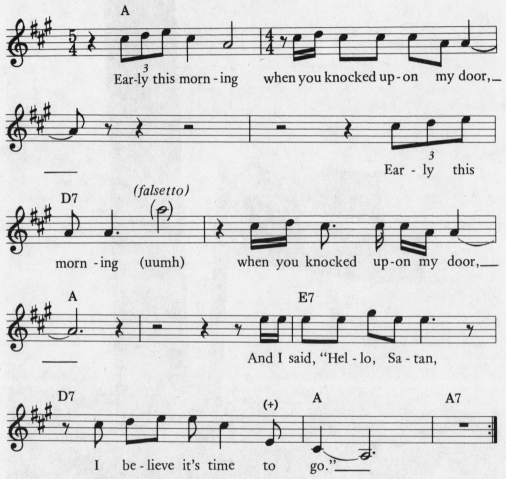

Me and the Devil was walking side by side,
Me and the Devil, uumh, was walking side by side,
I'm going to beat my woman until I get satisfied.

    Spoken: *Now baby, you know you ain't doing me right.*

She said she don't see why that I will dog her around,
She said she don't see why, uumh, that I will dog her around,
It must have be that old evil spirit so deep down in the ground.

You may bury my body down by the highway side,
    Spoken: *Baby, I don't care where you bury my body when I'm dead and gone.*
You may bury my body, uumh, down by the highway side,
So my old evil spirit can get a Greyhound bus and ride.

He returns, with this song, to the theme of the devil that began the session with *Hell Hound On My Trail*. Other singers had used the supernatural in their blues—Texas Alexander's *Blue Devil Blues* from 1928, Bessie Mae Smith's *Ghost Creepin' Blues* from 1927 among many others—but there seems to be a sense of desolation, of agony, in the blues Johnson sang about the devil. The final image, of his spirit catching a Greyhound bus, is startling in its combination of old beliefs and modern technology. The guitar is in regular tuning and he is playing in the key of A.

Stop Breakin' Down Blues

Recorded Dallas, June 20, 1937
Matrix number DAL 399-1
Original issue Vocalion 04002
Reissued on Columbia lp C30034

This is in a narrative blues form, with the first two vocal phrases in a faster rhythm and a kind of suspended harmony so that the singer can get more text into the verse. The last two lines follow each time as a refrain.

Key of original recording and transcription A.

Ev - er - y-time I'm walk-ing____ down the streets,

Some pret-ty ma-ma starts break-in' down with me. Stop break-in'

down, Yes,____ stop break-in' down.

The stuff I got-'ll bust your brains out, ba-by,

(umh)__ it-'ll make you lose your mind. __

I can't walk the streets now, can't consolate my mind,
Some no good woman, she starts breaking down,
Stop breaking down, please stop breaking down,*

Now you Saturday night women, you love to ape and clown,
You won't do nothing but tear a good man's reputation down,
Stop breaking down, please stop breaking down,*

Now I give my baby now the ninety-nine degree,
She jumped up and throwed her pistol down on me,
Stop breaking down, please stop breaking down,*

I can't start walking down the street,
But some pretty mama don't start breaking down with me,
Stop breaking down, yeh, stop breaking down,*

*Repeats last two lines from first verse as a refrain following each new verse.

Friars Point

Traveling Riverside Blues

Recorded Dallas, June 20, 1937
Matrix number DAL-400-2
Original issue Columbia lp 62456. This was unissued prior to its appearance on lp.

Key of original recording B, transposed to A.

If your man get per-son-al want to have your fun,—

If your man get per-son-al want to have your fun,—

Best come on back to Friars Point, ma-ma, and

bar-rel house all night long.——— I got

I got womens in Vicksburg, clean on into Tennessee,
I got womens in Vicksburg, clean on into Tennessee,
But my Friars Point rider now hops all over me.

I ain't going to state no color, but her front teeth crowned with gold,
I ain't going to state no color, but her front teeth is crowned with gold,
She got a mortgage on my body now, lien on my soul.

Lord I'm going to Rosedale, gonna take my rider by my side,
Lord I'm going to Rosedale, gonna take my rider by my side,
We can still barrelhouse, baby, 'cause it's on the river side.

80

Now you can squeeze my lemon 'til the juice run down my. . .
    Spoken: *'Til the juice run down my leg, baby, you know what I'm talking about.*
You can squeeze my lemon 'til the juice run down my leg,
    Spoken: *That's what I'm talking 'bout.*
But I'm going back to Friars Point, if I be rocking to my end.

Traveling Riverside Blues and *If I Had Possession Over Judgement Day* use the same melody and accompaniment, both of them sounding like something he learned from Son House. The guitar is in open G tuning, and is played with a slide or bottleneck. Although the harmonic changes are suggested in both the voice and the guitar the only strong harmonic resolution is on the lower strings of the guitar, when the slide is moved up the neck to play the dominant and subdominant root as a single insistent note. The introduction is one of the usual patterns he used in most of his songs, but the accompaniment has a doubled rhythm close to the style of something like Son's *Pony Blues.* Friars Point is a small, shabby town in a bend of the levee, its old main street of brick buildings boarded up and empty, its gasoline station—in 1972—still with a large sign saying "white" and "black" for the toilets. The black section is a cluster of shacks scattered along dirt streets south of the main section. It's on a local road west of Highway 61, south of the bridge over the Mississippi to Helena. Rosedale is further south, in a curve of the river on state route 1, twenty miles west of Cleveland, Mississippi. Charley Patton was living just outside of Cleveland when he died in the mid-thirties, and it was a crossroads for many blues singers.

Honeymoon Blues

Recorded Dallas, June 20, 1937
Matrix number DAL-401-
Original issue Vocalion 04002
Reissued on Columbia lp C30034

Key of original recording B♭, transposed to A.

Bet-ty Mae,___ Bet-ty Mae, you shall be my wife some day.___

Bet - ty Mae,___

___ Bet-ty Mae,___ you shall be my wife some day. I want a

lit - tle sweet girl ___

that will do an-y-thing that I say.___ Bet-ty Mae,

Betty Mae, you is my heartstrings, you is my destiny,
Betty Mae, you is my heartstrings, you is my destiny,
And you rolled across my mind, baby, each and every day.

Little girl, little girl, my life seems so misery,
Uumh, little girl, my life seems so misery,
Baby, I guess it must be love now, uumh lord, that's taking effect on me.

Some day I will return with my marriage license in my hand,
Some day I will return, uumh, with a marriage license in my hand.
I'm gonna take you for a honeymoon in some long, long distant land.

Love In Vain

Recorded Dallas, June 20, 1937
Matrix number DAL-402-1
Reissued on Columbia lp C30034

Key of original recording A♭, transposed to G.

When the train rolled up to the station, I looked her in the eye,
When the train rolled up to the station, and I looked her in the eye.
Well, I was lonesome, I felt so lonesome, and I could not help but cry,
All my love's in vain.

When the train, it left the station, there was two lights on behind,
When the train, it left the station, there was two lights on behind.
Well, the blue light was my blues, and the red light was my mind.
All my love's in vain.

Uumh, Willie Mae, Uumh, Willie Mae, Uumh, uumh, All my love's in vain.

Love In Vain, like *Hell Hound On My Trail*, is unique—there isn't anything in the blues like it. It is not in a standard blues form, but the theme and the musical style are completely within the blues idiom, and it is one of the most painfully beautiful blues love songs. It has become recently popular through the recording of it by the Rolling Stones, which is close to the original, but is slower in tempo and does not repeat the last line of the verse.

85

Milkcow's Calf Blues

Recorded Dallas, June 20, 1937
Matrix number DAL-403-2, 3
Original issue ARC 7-10-65, Vocalion 03665, Conqueror 8944
Reissued on Columbia lp 62456.

Key of original recording B♭, transposed to A.

Now your calf is hungry, I believe he needs to suck,
Now your calf is hungry, uumh, I believe he needs to suck,
But your milk is turning blue, uumh, I believe he's out of luck.

86

Now I feel like milking and my cow won't come,
I feel like churning and my milk won't turn,
I'm crying please, please, don't do me wrong,
If you see my milkcow, baby, now please drive her home.

My milkcow been rambling, uumh, for miles around,
My milkcow been rambling, uumh, for miles around,
Well, now she's been sucking some other man's bullcalf, uumh, in the strange
    man's town.

    This session was Johnson's last, and it was also his longest, ten songs recorded
at one time. The range of material recorded was very wide, from the
obsessiveness of *Hell Hound* to the blander Lonnie Johnson pieces, the open
bottleneck style of *Traveling Riverside* and the simple beauty of *Love In Vain*.
The last song he was to record, *Milkcow's Calf Blues,* uses the same melody and
accompaniment as *Terraplane Blues,* recorded at his first session seven months
before. It probably, like *Sweet Home Chicago,* derives from the recordings of
Kokomo Arnold, whose first release, *Milk Cow Blues* and *Old Original Kokomo
Blues* in late 1934, was very successful and widely imitated. Although the session
included two of his greatest songs it also included a number of more thinly
derivative pieces. It could mean that in a sense he did record the best of his
music—there was never to be any more, but there was, in a sad way, enough.